Contents

DRIFTING DOWN THROUGH DORSET
(song lyric)

I was travelling along, I was looking at the trees,
they lined the road, gave me shade,
seemed to know my needs,
I was thinking, thinking,
one day I'm gonna stay with these.

I was walking through the fields, I was lying on the ground
hearing hoofbeats, heartbeats,
distant from the town,
I was thinking, thinking,
this is where I want to be around.

> Drifting down through Dorset, feeling I belong,
> something I don't know just made me write this song.

I was driving down the lanes, I was searching for a home,
somewhere I could grow,
somewhere to be alone
I was thinking, thinking,
this is good, happy on my own.

I was circling the skies, I was swimming in the sea,
soaring over headlands, hilltops,
feeling oh so free,
I was thinking, thinking,
this must be meant to be.

> Drifting down through Dorset, feeling I belong,
> something I don't know just made me write this song.

Anne Peterson

ON WEYMOUTH SANDS

Yesterday, I wrote a poem
On Weymouth sands,
The sea washed it away.

Today, I wrote another poem
On Weymouth sands,
The sea washed it away again.

Tomorrow, I won't write a poem
On Weymouth sands.
I get the message.

Richard Green

3

GRANDFATHER'S SECRET AND MINE

(A fictionalised version of a Dorset event that took place in Victorian times)

I awoke, hearing a cart trundling past our cottage in the moonless night. Where was it going? And why? The Church clock chimed the midnight hour. Within seconds I pulled my dark coat over my pyjamas, stepped into my boots and crept outside, unheard and unseen. I could tell from the sound which way the cart was going so I walked downhill, past the last cottage and saw that it had stopped by the Church gate. Men were unloading barrels from it. Knowing a track that runs alongside the wall I followed it, then climbed over where stones have crumbled, making it lower. Tall yew trees that darken the churchyard in daylight had become huge shrouds. I was grateful for their protection. I stood close to one, engulfed in darkness, invisible.

There were six men at least, all hauling the barrels up the steep, hard path to the Church. They said little and when they spoke it was to say bad words, the sort that my grandfather has banned. Grandfather is a committed Christian, a churchwarden, parish clerk and a highly respected man.

Standing by the two heavy horses was another man – well, a boy, about my size. Somewhere above and behind me an owl hooted. One of the horses whinnied in reply.

'Shut up or I'll thump you,' said the boy handler.

The horse did shut up but the owl didn't. I half turned, hoping to see it, then froze. Someone was approaching. The shuffling footsteps stopped; then I heard a trickle. I closed my eyes thinking if I can't see, I can't be seen – a game I played when I was little.

'Takin' a leak, Ben?' said someone on the path, swinging a lantern.

'Shut it. We've finished 'aven't we?' The man close to me started to walk away; then he stumbled against a gravestone.

'Steady, mate, oughta be in bed at your age,' said the other one. 'You awl right?'

'Wot, wiv all that money comin'? Course I'm awl right.'

'Yeah, but you gotta live to enjoy it.'

The lantern was swinging closer.

4

'Wot the 'ell? Grab 'im, mate.'

A hand clutched my left arm; then another one grabbed me on the other side. I tried to back away but the protective tree had become my enemy, blocking my escape. The lantern was now close to my face.

It's a lad,' the holder exclaimed 'Wot you doin' 'ere?'

'I 'eard the cart go by and I was curious,' I said, my voice a bit trembly.

'Well, we'll take you to the Guv. I guess 'e'll be more furious than curious.'

The men marched me up to the church door. Inside the porch was a tall, imposing figure. I gasped; it was Grandfather. He told the men to let me go and that all was well. As they walked away I couldn't tell if they were chuckling or grumbling.

'Come inside, lad, and I'll tell 'ee what's what.' I followed Grandfather into the transept where a few candles flickered, relieving the darkness but I saw no barrels.

'Where are they, the barrels?' I asked, after explaining why I was there.

'Now, lad, you've stumbled on a very special secret,' he replied.

'You know about Communion wine – well, we've just had a delivery but all hidden away.'

'But why at night? And why is it a secret?'

'Because the vicar thinks the Lord supplies it and I'd hate to disappoint him. Never does the Communion wine run out. It's my gift to the community and I don't want anyone to know about it.'

He took something from his pocket and pressed it into my hand. I stared, thrilled and surprised – it was a glittering gold coin.

'That's very generous, Grandpa. I promise I'll keep your secret.'

'I know you will – you'll always keep your word. You're a good boy.'

And I am keeping my word, only sharing the secret with my diary.

Note: Charles kept his word but, after his death, the diary was read and the source of his highly respected grandfather's wealth and generosity was revealed.

Pauline Morphy

* * * * * * * * * * * * * * * *

A hard-drinking native of Stoborough
reformed and grew soberer and soberer.
   But one night he lapsed,
    drank too much and collapsed,
then stuck out his tongue like a cobra.

A Sloane Ranger staying in Corfe
enjoyed the odd dip to cool orfe.
   At Studland she strayed
    through the dunes, where she sayed:
'If thet's what they do heah, Ai'm orfe!'

John Barclay

TIME TRAVELLING

From the Car

The B3070 from Stoborough towards East Lulworth is, to begin with, deceptively ineffectual and almost nondescript; yet another Dorset backwater which winds its graceful way through leafy woods and dells, lulling the unknowing voyager into a childhood recall of I-spy security: something beginning with T perhaps?

Well into the first decades of the twentieth century, travellers foregoing the pleasures of the seaside disembarked the London train at Wareham and passed this way by the pony and trap that collected them from the station. Not that there was a plethora of trippers; those who came were largely family members and guests staying over at the big houses: the Bond's Elizabethan manor down at Tyneham or their cousins' Gothic pile at Creech Grange. We're just passing through Creech now. The way steepens sharply but there is room to pull over on the bend and look back at the stately mansion with its neat parklands waiting patiently for sheep and deer to complete the landscape. The Bonds have gone of course. These days, the Grade 1 listed building is owned by the former chairman of Bournemouth's football team; a man who, like the Horseshoe Bats that also reside there, spends a lot of time hidden away with the occasional swooping and diving necessary to avoid unwanted visitors. But this is not our stop. Onward up the hill, through the last of the beginning-with-T trees and suddenly we are at the top of the world! Neither warning nor indication of the panorama of magnificence that awaits the unsuspecting has been suggested. It's shocking in its powerfulness and intensity. Fortunately, those who journeyed this way latterly realised the views would be far too distracting and have constructed a small but handy car park in order that we can replenish our momentarily lost breath with some healthy sea air. And there in front is the sea where Portland, strange stony home to two or three of Her Majesty's prisons, sits like a great Jurassic sea monster nurturing its ill-tempered young.

Turning anti-clockwise, the long-to-be-lost-in hills and valleys of Purbeck roll lushly down to the hidden beach of Kimmeridge, where a £5 road toll and a dearth of pubs, shops and Mary Anning literature has kept this ammonite-strewn gem tourist-free – temporarily perhaps, as lottery funding has just been designated to open a fossil museum in the village. Round to the church towers of Kingston and Langton;

bypassing St Aldhelm's Head and its bizarrely orientated and apparently dateless chapel; past the bucket-and-spade brigade at and on to the crumbling castle of Corfe. Upwards to Brenscombe Hill and onto Nine Barrow Down; all the time edged by more and more sea until finally the water meets the shore at Sandbanks and is strangely wrong-footed by the glorious Poole Harbour which sits smugly in the knowledge of being the second biggest of the natural variety IN THE WORLD.

Crowned with islands, home to the Famous Five and the even more secret world of onshore oil and pipelines, edged by the verdant forest of Rempstone; onto the golf links where, in a time before bunkers and clubs intruded, Ms Blyton held court to small fans whilst her daughters remained exiled in their rooms; over to the water meadows and marshlands and in full circle to Monkey World: a playground for primates amidst the ruined heathland, hacked, ploughed and trashed by the war machine of Bovington but still precariously interwoven with tiny roads. On one these, T.E. Lawrence, having exchanged his camel for a Brough Superior, rode like a latter-day Buzz Lightyear into infinity and beyond. This is the workplace of the Ministry of Defence and here on Creech Barrow, overlooking the Neolithic, the way is dotted with red flags and placards bearing skulls and crossed bones. And just down the road is the turning to Tyneham where, according to today's sign, the range-walks are fortuitously open.

Rewind

Into the valley rode at least six hundred: lorries, tanks, jeeps and motorcycles – all the paraphernalia necessary for the successful requisitioning of a small Dorset village. For, hidden away down this long and winding lane, one can find the remains of 'The Village That Died For England'. In brief, Churchill commandeered Tyneham and its surrounding 7,500 acres, including nearby Worbarrow Bay, for troops to practise land and sea strategies in preparation for the eventual D-Day landings. The two-hundred-and-fifty-two villagers were told that their enforced evacuation would be temporary. Immediately prior to Christmas 1943, they left to enjoy the festivities and spend the rest of the war with relatives in other Dorset villages. That they left willingly and in the belief of the transitory nature of their displacement is attested to by a notice pinned to the door of the church; a facsimile of which remains in place:

Please treat the church and houses with care; we have given up our homes where many of us have lived for generations to help win the war and keep men free. We shall return one day and thank you for treating our village kindly.

The word was broken and in 1948 a compulsory order was issued by the War Office, subsequently the Ministry of Defence, to the effect that Tyneham would remain in its hands. Today, what is left of the village and surrounding heathland and chalk downs acts as a firing range for the army. The church remains sacrosanct and the one-room schoolhouse is now home to a continuous and disembodied nature lesson of times past, recreated by the military of today. And herein lays the irony of lies: for in spite of, or perhaps due to, the removal of humanity and seventy ensuing years of constant shelling, nature and wildlife have regained a hold on this place of sadness. Thus, the focus changes to one of absence in the landscape.

Fast Forward

Autumn. Behind the seven-bar gate of Buffknolls, the old farm track leads between two slightly raised dips before turning under winter-inspired hawthorn that is heavy with blood-red berries. Alongside the picture-perfect pastoral, wallpaper cows graze in the pleasant sun below Flowers Barrow which, in old age, sits murmuring to itself against a clear blue sky. From over the top of the inner ridge, floating on currents of air, buzzards mingle with hang-gliders. An almost-Arcadia in which we could walk and dream with ghosts; except that on the gate is a large red and white sign warning that this is a firing range and entry without clearance is forbidden.

Down through fields and woods whose names have faded with time: Limekiln Plantation, Old Cowleaze, Rook Grove, Three Acres until we arrive in today's official picnic spot at West Mead; kindly designated as a safety zone by the Royal Artillery. As I walk back to the village, the wind sashays through many varieties of trees dressed in ill-behaved leaves that are now turning secondary-red-yellow-orange-brown. Brambles, confused by twenty-first century seasons, still bear stubborn blackberries. A solitary celandine stands in discordant sympathy. Likewise, as I cross the bridge over an innocent-looking brook – Danger! Deep Water – one red dragonfly dares to perch out of time on a shiny holly bush. Many scarlet berries forecast a harsh winter: a thoughtful but hardly relevant warning in a place where no-one lives.

9

Excuse me? The Goulds live here in the aptly named Gardeners' Cottage; the apostrophe being so situated because it's the home of all the gardeners who have worked at Tyneham House over the years; not just one. A box for wild birds still clings to the trunk of the giant oak in their front garden, although I suspect it may not be an original. The fact that the roof of the house is missing is a small clue to what has passed here. And those roofs were comprised of stone tiles that didn't just blow away in the wind. Blown away they were though. Anyway, come in. Just look at the view through what remains of the windows: a herd of compliant cows wandering in the grassland of Long Mead.

We take the back path that straggles behind the church and thus reach the bullet-scarred rectory, inside which I find a display of photographs taken by the American army in 1943. No fools, those boys: they could see the point of preservation. A few weeds and a handful of moss have broken through the slabs on the floor. Outside, a gigantic conifer clings in peril to the sky. The ornamental pond, which the optimistic Patrick Wright noted was well maintained in his celebrated account of the village history, has since become throttled by unidentifiable antediluvian foliage. Sitting ambivalentlyon a bench, in what once passed for a garden, I look to the hills of Gold Down which are marked with numbered firing targets. Suddenly, three roe deer appear in the nearby field. Spotting us, they quickly sidle into the trees just as the wind drops sufficiently to hear hidden birdsong.

The path from the rectory to Laundry Cottage is muddy and our sinking footprints join those of Maria Elques, her daughter and son and three grandchildren; the washers of other people's clothes. Bright green ferns that have yet to wither and die choke Maria's garden. They offer those of us devoid of deer-spotting deer-stalkers enough camouflage to regard the herd that, with safety in numbers and the new presence of the stag, has now evolved into a tail-swishing-still-anxious huddle. If I stand here long enough without turning round, the roof of Laundry Cottage will exist once more as Maria trundles up the path with her buckets of water, momentarily noting the deer that have been grazing in Flagon Grass for a century or more. She wonders whether this spring they will allow her daffodils to flower long enough to add to the Mothering Sunday spray.

Emerging from Rookery Wood into the tell-tale sunlight that lets you know the sea is near, even when you can't yet see or smell it, we wander by Shepherds' Cottage whose interior, in summers since the war, has been tastefully furnished with bright pink wallflowers. I pause to peer into the gloom of the telephone box hoping someone might call with news from the other side. The only message available reads 'I am on war work. If you must use me, be brief!' A large brown spider, having spun a thick web across one corner, has trapped a million miniscule prisoners to entertain her on the long, lonely winter nights ahead.

Bill Douglas was here in the eighties, directing the first half of *Comrades*. Despite maintaining a small cottage industry based on the Martyrs, which, year after year witnesses a growing parade of union-affiliated history processing along the one and only road, Tolpuddle was deemed far too modernised to be a realistic setting. Tyneham, however, was just the job having never been given the opportunity to move forward along a temporal line. Obviously, Douglas encountered a slight set-back owing to the fact that the cottages had been considerably damaged by constant firing, being thus in a state of disrepair far exceeding that of the hovels originally inhabited by Loveless and his pals. No problem; facades were erected for each of the buildings, hopefully with the blessing of the construction workers and allied trades, for the duration of the filming. Then they removed them and went home, taking their own ghosts with them.

We still have another mile to walk down to Worbarrow Bay and set off towards West Mead and the site of the farmhouse. Ahead, the fearless can stride up to Gad Cliff and along the coastal path to Cornwall, but we are making a right turn past the old corn grounds. To our right is Tyneham Gwyle, an old Dorset name for a wooded glen near the mouth of a stream. First listed in 1648, the Gwyle is probably hundreds of years older. In fact, it looks positively primeval with its still green creepers creeping their way around gnarled lichen-covered trunks that tower above mosses and ferns. On this now darkening October day, the wood seems eerily silent belying its hospitality to stoats and Sika, green woodpecker and insects; and in the spring, bluebells and Dog's Mercury and wild garlic. When the big house was occupied, wild flowers were always protected in Tyneham; even the woodmen who trimmed the banks were forbidden from cutting them. Now, the ancient hedgerows that once served to keep out livestock are, like the dead tank on the opposite hill, forgotten and abandoned.

The Gwyle was the link between the village and the sea in ways other than simply providing a playground for those who, having been released from the schoolhouse at noon, were on their way to afternoon bathing. Alongside the stream, withies were cultivated for local fishermen to weave into lobster pots; whilst eels that swam in the water were captured by children and used as bait for mackerel fishing off Worbarrow Tout. In fact, as the clouds are gathering, and we still have other ghosts to listen to, we hurry off down to the sea. I leave the imagined voices of the young behind, muffled by the sound of distant firing from the range at Lulworth. Ahead, I hear the call of David Miller's wooden leg tap-tapping on the rocks.

Most of the Miller family were fishermen by tradition but the first dwelling we reach is the beer house run by a maverick cousin. David hobbled about his business, often in the company of George Selby, the postman. Having made his morning deliveries, George left his pony and trap at the back of David's abode and spent his days working on his allotment or helping the fishermen. And help was always gratefully received because Worbarrow Bay was a particularly rich ground spawning pollock, herrings, sprats, red and grey mullet, pilchards and mackerel in their thousands. On moonlit nights the men went conger-fishing but their biggest source of income was the lobsters and crabs that the dealers in Wareham craved on behalf of their customers in distant cities. When these men left, they took with them all their secret weather- and sea-lore leaving the fish behind to be worried by allied landing craft.

From the conical Tout, wearing its target number three with some embarrassment, the bay sweeps round past Cow Corner to the inlet of Arish Mell where Churchill was once photographed commanding the troops without a hint of incongruity. The beach is comprised partly of sand but largely of pebbles. If you know where to look, you can discover luminous green stones that have been polished by thousands of tides. The bay is enclosed by cliffs hundreds of feet high, on the top of which we can see brave or foolhardy ramblers on the best of England's green and pleasant. It's difficult to imagine anywhere further removed from the Normandy theatre. I look down on this landscape of absence from the ruins of Coastguard Cottages, inside which a leafless tree has grown, turning its bent length inwards, away from decades of stormy seas. The coastguard was withdrawn in 1912 and William Bond had the buildings destroyed rather than let them become the holiday homes of outsiders. He thought he could forestall intrusion.

The late afternoon sky hangs heavily over waves which are crashing onto the shoreline. The lonely beach must be left for sunnier Sundays with new generations of children and I turn tail, wending my way back along the Gwyle. There's just time to take a look at the old barn back at West Mead. This year, it was open for midsummer's eve entertainment for the first time since the war. Ladies, dressed in the garb of long-gone-days, sold nosegays and men sporting specially grown sideburns distributed cider. Songs from old Wessex were rendered and Edward Fox, famous resident of Creech, performed for the delight of the audience. Outside, someone has invested their time carefully in the old walled garden. On that summer evening, scented sweet-peas clambered up and along the stones and welcome bees hovered over banks of lavender.

Today, the place is closed once more and, even with the passing of just a few months, it's as though that evening, along with all the others, is nothing more than the dream of a dream.

The last of the day's visitors have left and we must also make our way home before the gate is closed on Tyneham for another week, another season, another time. It matters little how long we wait before returning; the only changes will be those wrought by nature.

Alison Green

13

DORSET CURSUS

Every day
I move these stones
From down there
To up here
Day after day
From daybreak to nightfall
I move these stones.
I don't know why
If there's a plan
They haven't told me.
I can't see the point of it
But if I want to eat
I have to move these stones.

Some days the mist is so thick
I can't see the top nor the bottom.
I can just hear the slow drip of water from the branches
But some days sunlight breaks suddenly through the leaves
And there's a kind of beauty.
White light reflecting off the chalk
And sparking off the flint
As the mound snakes away across the hill.
Maybe that's purpose enough.

Liz Magee

Note: The Dorset Cursus is a neolithic monument which once stretched for 10 kilometres through the undulating chalkland of Cranborne Chase, from Martin Down to Thickthorn Down (both near the A354 road).

MASTER OF THE UNIVERSE

The gentleman of the road walks with difficulty
on crutches to my left.
I pass in my car between him and the gypsy pony
tethered to my right.
Fleetingly, I am aware of both and continue the short
journey
to my job beside the sea,

where some hours later, he catches up,
sits in the shelter of my hut,
as I issue permits to jet-skiers, anxiously watching
homing pigeons,
held up by bad weather in their lorry,
awaiting release.

Systematically, he sifts through the contents
of a litter bin,
oblivious to the stares of tourists and fishermen,
concentrating intently,
gaining maximum benefit and enjoyment
from minimum food.

Wonder, can I offer crusts brought for the pony
without giving offence?
Answer comes as he takes
a butt from his pocket, lights it,
inhales deeply with obvious pleasure
and takes in the view,

walks on limping, an unlikely icon of freedom,
leaving me prisoner to my job,
pigeons unable to fly,
gypsy pony still tethered,
answerable to no-one,
master of his universe.

Susan Northcott

TREASURE

Many tales exist about Winterbourne Manley: how the Romans conquered the Saxons who held the mound nearby; how King Charles 1st hid in a cave, now nowhere to be found; how Granny Gunter cursed the people of the town with her last breath before being consumed by flames. One of the strangest and possibly the truest, for I, John Knapp, for one, believe it, is that of the treasure trove guarded by otters.

I was catching the bus to Weymouth; it was raining hard and the flimsy imitation of a bus shelter gave no protection, so that I anticipated, at best, a wet backside, and, at worst, pneumonia. Behind me, others, who had the sense, on a wet day, not to arrive early for a bus that was always late, were catching up with their days' news. One man, in a turned back cap, the brim of which was funnelling water at speed down the gap between his shirt and his anorak, had a particularly strident voice. Even in my own world of planning my trip, I could not help over-hearing him:

'BBC camera men have been about early this morning by the Manley,' he alleged, nudging his neighbour. 'It's not otters they're after; it's the gold. But they won't get it. Otters is cunning; they turns the stones over and over so's we can't find what's underneath, and anyone who goes into that part of the river gets caught in the weed . . . there have been drownings,' he added, with a wink.

A woman, who had been trying to protect herself from the deluge with an umbrella that kept folding itself inside out, gave up her task and turned to the previous speaker:

'I've heard the gold was the booty from a highway robbery in the eighteenth century.'

Another woman joined in: 'How did it get in the Manley?'

The original speaker turned to her. 'My grandmother told me that the highwayman tried to escape and was drowned by the weed.'

Just then the 152 arrived and in the queue for tickets, I missed the next words of my fellow passengers, but by now I was fascinated and managed to find a seat in front of the loud-voiced man and the woman with the inside-out umbrella.

I was entranced by their conversation, for almost everyone in Manley Regis knew something of the tale and, as I'd lived there since a child, I knew most of them. Always, there was treasure in the river, in the deepest weediest hollow, where even the fishermen dared not wade, had been tossed into the water by a jewel thief who had stolen it from one of the grand houses at the top of town; others that it was a hoard left by a miser in a never-to-be-repeated particularly dry summer. The man who could do this must not only have been a miser but was a fool, as in the last few years our river has not merely been a winter waterway, as the name of our town suggests, but at times a full-bodied torrent.

The pair had little more to add to my knowledge of the subject but, whilst I carried out my business in Weymouth, ideas for treasure retrieval buzzed in my head. It would be too bad if the BBC found the treasure and we deserving residents of Manley didn't get anything.

I had noted that there was to be a film about the Manley otters on television in a month or two and, when it finally showed in the paper, I could hardly wait to see it. I had prepared myself: I had a strong magnifying glass and had banished my wife, Jane, to cook supper. She was very curious as to the glass, but I refused to be drawn on my sudden interest in Natural History.

Every detail of the shots taken by underwater cameras, I perused with four hundred per cent magnification. Yes, there were otters turning pebbles, and suddenly a shaft of light focussed on something shiny, but, before I could move my magnifier to the spot, it had gone. At that moment, my wife came into the lounge and found me bent over the telly.

'What on earth are you doing?' she enquired. "Supper's nearly ready and I could do with some help."

It's funny how women think that a retired husband is ready to become a junior housekeeper, I thought. I pretended that she had left a smear when dusting the screen.

Despite being interrupted, I had formulated a plan for finding the treasure. First, I would need a boat; then I'd need a pole with a net on the end; a flashlight would be a good idea.

For the newspapers, I prepared this story; I would be famous and, with luck, rich. My old work-mate, Tom Briggs, had a boat, a little thing that he'd been patching up. It should be light enough to carry and he never kept his shed locked. With any luck there would be a suitable pole somewhere and I already had a flash-light. So I was all set up for treasure hunting. Tonight's the night. This has to be the night. As Jane is off at her mother's dealing with the latest catastrophe that that old dear has invented.

I have provisioned myself with a headlamp as well as the flashlight; this document I'm leaving on my desk ready for publication. No point getting it wet.

[story continues by Jane Knapp, as told to the Manley Echo]

The canoe must have proved heavier than he'd thought, for there were deep footprints on the path to the river. How he could see his way at all, I don't know, under the edge of Tom Briggs' Kayak. It must have been quite near the water that he fell and banged his head on a tree. He was lucky that my mum rang up and said that she didn't need me after all and that I'd followed him to see what feather-brained scheme he had thought of this time.

It's only mild concussion, but he'll be in Weymouth hospital for a while. I've been catching up on the latest news about our otters: they have apparently been playing with oyster shells, left in the river by the Romans, it's said. Of course, in the light caught by the underwater filming, they sparkled a bit.

I think I'll take advantage of John's stay in hospital to learn a bit about Roman History; 'though I don't think he'll be in hospital long, as I'm told that he's giving the nurses a hard time. I hope he'll be pleased with his twenty-four hours of fame.

M C Wood

Young and old members of the community of Wareham came together to create a tree out of clay, each leaf celebrating the life of the individual who fashioned it. The following poem was written to mark the completion of the tree and its 'planting' in the garden of Wareham Library on 24th May 2013.

TREES

Gentle, long-living giants,
purifying our air,
sheltering birds and beetles,
bearing fruit, giving shade,
soft carpets of leaves,
places to hide, climb and play.
Seedlings, saplings and sturdy trunks,
young and old can grow together.

We have made a tree
of clay – bark and leaves
shaped and decorated
by children and seniors
working side by side,
so that here in this garden,
book-lovers and visitors,
young and old will smile together.

We want our tree to flourish,
branch out, bear fruit –
not apples or chestnuts,
but new ideas that are fun
for both generations
to try – so that,
sharing these things,
young and old may bloom together.

John Barclay

EDWARD, BOY KING, SAINT AND MARTYR

More is known about Edward's death than his life. He was born in about 962 AD. His father was King Edgar the Peaceable, a great-great-grandson of Alfred the Great. Edward's mother died shortly after he was born. Edgar took a second wife, called Elfryth, who bore him a second son, Ethelred (later King Ethelred, known as 'the Unready'). This is a confusing period of history to study because most of the kings and queens have names beginning with 'E'.

Edward had not long been a teenager when he succeeded his father in 975. Because of his age, Edward had little influence over the earldormen (aldermen), who were the highest authorities in the shires. His stepmother Queen Elfryth therefore must have wielded considerable power in the land. The events that followed confirmed the unsurprising fact that she wanted her stepson out of the way so that her own son, Ethelred could seize the throne.

In 979, when the young King Edward was no more than 18, after hunting in Wareham Forest, he retired to Elfryth's lodge in

Corfe Village. (The Castle, whose ruins we see today, was not built until the 11th Century.) It is reported that when Edward arrived, the Queen's servants greeted him with a goblet of mead and while he drank they stabbed him in the back.

He soon died of his wound and his body was dumped in a hut nearby, where an old blind woman was living. The building was said to become filled with a bright light and the woman regained her sight. This was the first miracle surrounding the King's demise; others followed.

One version of what happened next has the King's corpse thrown down a well, where it lay for a year. When recovered, the body had a beautiful aroma, while the water remained clear and pure. What's more it possessed healing properties, particularly for blind people and lepers.

A more feasible legend claims that the body was hidden in an unmarked grave on Wareham Heath and again wasn't discovered for a year. A bright light shone over the site and a spring gushed forth with healing properties. The King's body was then lifted and interred in the church at Wareham. Later, the new King, Ethelred, had Edward's body moved to Shaftesbury Abbey where it was entombed.

This act of decency was in marked contrast to his mother's earlier treachery. The fact that at no time was Edward's death investigated or anyone charged with his murder, seems to confirm that guilt lay, and was known to lie, at the hands of a figure too powerful to challenge.

While Edward's remains were on their way to Shaftesbury, a further miracle is recorded, the curing of two lepers, who touched the coffin as it passed. Edward was canonised and given his own saint's day, March 18th. In the reign of Henry VIII, Shaftesbury Abbey was broken up during the dissolution of the monasteries. Edward's relics had been hidden to avoid desecration and they remained on the site until the 1930s, when they were transferred to the Eastern Orthodox Church at Brookland near Woking in Surrey. Today, an image of him can be seen in Corfe Castle.

Mike Lawrence

Note: Visitors to Wimborne Minster can see the stained glass depicting Edward the Martyr in the large window in the North Transept; third panel from the left. He is shown with a young face in contrast to the more elderly Saints near him.

LOVERS' TIFF

We wander along the tide line
as dusk begins to swathe
the rocks beyond the headland
and soften approaching waves.
On the horizon streaks of gold
tell of the departing sun
and Old Man Moon is brightening
but is he the only one?

We may be entering No Man's Land,
the distance now so great
between us, like a chasm,
and to fall could be our fate.
We must continue to argue
for to languish could mean the end,
a fathomless drop into silence
from which we might never ascend.

How good to agree to disagree,
to fight for a personal stance,
and bravely argue one's point of view
then exchange a sudden glance
that says we are as different
as nettles from scented flowers,
and yet the love we share
can go on for hours and hours.

Is the coastal beauty,
our beloved Durdle Door,
offering us a welcome
to come and share it all?
And brave the harshness of a storm
as nature's clever ploy
to show us that the love that's true
is there in every form?

Pauline Morphy

JANET'S LUCKY DAY

It wasn't a good evening for motorway driving. Rain lashed down, gale-force winds seemed to want to lift the little car bodily off the road and passing traffic splashed blinding spray onto the windscreen mocking the feeble efforts of the wipers.

Janet Parsons leant forward in the driving seat, peering into the darkness. A glamorous 23 year-old, she was more short-sighted than she cared to admit but hated contact lenses and refused to wear spectacles. Sexy though Janet undoubtedly was, her appearance was slightly old-fashioned, rather like the cool blonde in a fifties movie. It wasn't the bad weather that was worrying Janet, though. In the space of an hour that lunchtime she had dumped her clingy boy-friend (by text message) walked out of her job (leaving a rude note for her boss) and abandoned her studio flat (owing six weeks rent).

A triple whammy enough to daunt most people but Janet wasn't at all daunted – she felt happy and free. And why shouldn't she feel happy and free when in the boot of her Ford Fiesta, as it made its way down the M3, battered by unfriendly elements, was £60,000 in cash?

Janet had been alone in the office of the small accountancy firm in Camberley where she worked. Her boss, Roley Jenkins, the senior (and only) partner had gone out to lunch.

A remarkable figure appeared in the doorway. He was tall and thin, wore a long khaki raincoat, under which could be glimpsed striped pyjama trousers and tattered carpet slippers. On his head was an ancient stetson hat so you could see little of his face but it was possible to tell that he had a rather moth-eaten straggly beard and dirty shoulder length grey hair. A sight that would alarm most people – but Janet wasn't alarmed. She knew that this strange being was Lord Mounthatchet, one of the richest men in England and a client of the firm.

'I'm going away for a while, I think,' he said vaguely. 'So…er…well could you look after this for me, my dear?'

He dumped an old holdall on the desk.

'What's in it?'

Lord Mounthatchet looked puzzled. He thought for a while.

'Money, I think.'

Janet peeked inside the holdall. There *was* money inside. A LOT of money.

'That's all right, Lord Mounthatchet. We'll take care of it for you.'

'Take care of what?' asked Lord Mounthatchet. He gazed distract-edly out of the window for a few moments.

'Ah well,' he said wistfully. 'I can't stay here all night. I've got to be going . . . er . . . somewhere.'

He looked at his wrist. 'Good God, I'm already late!' he exclaimed and in great haste stumbled out of the door and lurched down the street. A huge grin spread over Janet's face. This really was her lucky day. The *'Daily Express'* horoscope had been right. She quickly counted the money. £60,000.

Roley Jenkins was in his late forties, fat, greasy, physically repulsive and continually lecherous as Janet had discovered on several occasions when he had sat her on his knee and slid his podgy hand up her thigh. He was also a crook and had been helping himself to large amounts of his clients' money. Janet had found out and had thought of contacting the police. But what good would that do her?

Now she had something to bargain with – Lord Mounthatchet's cash! She and Roley could go into the embezzling business together. They would make an excellent team. Both were avaricious, mean, self-centred and totally without moral scruples. But Janet had an advantage – she was cleverer.

She quickly typed a note:

> 'Roley, you slimy, fat freak. I'm just taking a break for a few days. I MIGHT inform the rozzers of your amateurish swindling activities, or I might not – haven't decided yet. Up yours! Janet

Then she sent the text message dumping her boy-friend. Janet didn't go back to her flat – she could buy anything she needed on the way. She would head for Bournemouth. Have a night on the town and tomorrow, maybe take the ferry to France. She would wait a week or two before contacting Roley. Let the bastard sweat.

Janet went up to the desk of the Delta, a hotel she had picked completely at random. There was a dark-haired young man on duty. He was slim and had a pale, rather hatchet-shaped face and, Janet supposed, wasn't really all that bad looking. But there was something sinister about his eyes – which were coal black – that seemed to bore right through her and make her flesh creep. In fact, the young man, Plantagenet Smith, wasn't a mere receptionist; he owned the hotel, supposedly in partnership with his mother, though nobody had ever seen her.

'Let me show you to your room,' he said. 'Number 39.'

When they arrived, Plantagenet seemed reluctant to leave. Janet thought that perhaps he was waiting for a tip.

'I can see that you are here alone. Would you like to come out for a drink with me later?'

Janet shuddered. 'No, thank you,' she said politely.

Plantagenet Smith looked rather crestfallen and slunk out of the room. Janet did not see the look of insane hatred that crossed his face as soon as he had shut the door.

'What a loser!' thought Janet. Never mind; she was ready to have some fun. She would try the casino. It would be amusing to try to beat the odds and see if she could make her pile of money grow.

Plantagenet Smith could hardly control his jealousy and rage. How dare that cheap stuck-up tart refuse to come out with him. She had talked to him as though he was dirt. He would show her. Plantagenet waited in the corridor. In a few moments he heard a gurgling sound coming from one of the hot water pipes. He knew what this meant. Someone was taking a shower. The person in Room 39 was taking a shower. *Janet* was taking a shower! Using his pass key, Plantagenet entered the room. He could hear the rushing of the water and see the outline of Janet's naked body behind the shower curtain. One of the perks of being a hotelier is that you can always get hold of a sharp knife with no questions asked. He walked swiftly across Room 39 and ripped open the shower curtain. Janet turned and gasped in horror as Plantagenet Smith raised the knife to strike.

In the kitchen of the Delta Hotel, Charlie Loomis was morosely stirring the sauce for the *bocuf bourgignon*. He was 26 and Head Chef of the Delta Hotel. Not bad for a fairly young man, but Charlie felt he should be Head Chef of somewhere classier such as the Royal Bath or the Carlton. Unfortunately he had left the employment of both of those establishments after blazing rows with the management.

As Charlie stirred away, he noticed something dripping from the ceiling. Damn. Room 39. That was always happening. Someone had taken a shower with the curtain open and now water was going into his precious sauce. Charlie was about to storm up to the room and give the guest a piece of his mind. Then he noticed that it WASN'T water – he caught one of the drops on his finger. BLOOD. He tasted the sauce. Interesting. The blood gave a distinctive flavour to the sauce, an exciting tang. Charlie calmed down and a thoughtful expression came over his face. He kept on stirring and the blood kept on dripping.

Jefferson Clutterbuck sat moodily in the dining room of the Delta Hotel. A wizened, hunched, permanently-angry man, he was restaurant critic of the *Pretentious Foodie Monthly*. Jefferson was only in the Delta because the editor of the magazine had once stayed there – on a 'dirty weekend' with Busty Brenda, his voluptuous, mini-skirt-wearing secretary. Not only did the editor fail to get his leg over but he found the food completely inedible.

'Get down there, Jefferson and see if the cuisine really is that disgusting,' he ordered. 'And, no you can't take Busty Brenda.'

The restaurant critic was therefore in an even fouler temper than usual and groaned at the thought of the *Boeuf Bourgignon*. He knew what to expect – lumps of gristle floating in an even lumpier *Own Brand Ready-mix Red Wine Gravy*. But when the meal arrived it was, to Jefferson's astonishment, absolutely delicious. He wrote a glowing review for the *Pretentious Foodie Monthly*. The reputation of the Delta Hotel soared and the place was nearly always full of people wanting to sample the exquisite and unique sauces. And not only the sauces. Most guests said that they had never tasted a more flavoursome *chicken fricassée* and the *veal escalopes* were so tender that many professional cooks tried to get Charlie Loomis to tell them his secret. But Charlie would never say.

Plantagenet Smith kept Janet's £60,000 in a strongbox under his bed. It was his personal property. He had *earned* that money. He was damned if he was going to put it into the business. Not that he needed to. Janet's unfortunate demise and the resulting dramatic improvement in the standard of the hotel's cuisine brought great prosperity to the Delta, which remains an outstanding commercial success to this day.

To ensure that the reputation of the Delta Hotel remains high, a constant supply of victims is required. Fortunately, Plantagenet Smith has a talent for homicide. It is always said that the first murder is the most difficult psychologically and Plantagenet *was* a little tense before he stabbed Janet. After that, each killing was pure enjoyment.

You might imagine that a large number of guests vanishing from the same hotel would cause suspicion. But Plantagenet is very selective. Single people who, like Janet, walk in off the street are good because no-one knows they are staying at the hotel. Illicit lovers are better (Plantagenet can easily detect these) as they always check in under false names. Best of all are foreign tourists. Owing to the total chaos of the British Passport Control System it is impossible to prove that these ill-fated individuals have ever set foot in the country – let alone have been anywhere near the Delta Hotel.

Most people would think that, in this digital age, records of any guest failing to check out in a normal manner must appear on the hotel's computer. Far from it.

'Doctoring' the Delta's database is literally child's play for Plantagenet's 14 year-old nephew, who is on bail fighting extradition for gaining illegal access to the main computer of the Icelandic Ministry of Defence. Okay, so it isn't the Pentagon but, hey, he's only a kid and every hacker has to start somewhere.

Staying at the Delta Hotel is, therefore, quite a risky business. Beware, particularly of any attractive offer to entice you there, such as a *'Special Exclusive Bargain Break'* or an on-line lottery where the prize is *'A weekend for two at the Delta'* – tempting though it may seem. Rather than sitting in the restaurant READING the menu, you might easily end up ON the menu. Take my advice. Give the Delta Hotel a miss and go to a holiday camp instead.

Note: While all the events described in this story actually happened, many of the names have had to be changed to protect the guilty. For instance, you won't find a *'Delta Hotel'* in Bournemouth and there are no such people as *'Janet Parsons'* and *'Jefferson Clutterbuck.'* There isn't a magazine called *'The Pretentious Foodie Monthly'* though sometimes I feel there ought to be. I, myself, feature in the narrative. Of course I can't reveal my true identity but I CAN let you know the name I assume in the story. It's *'Plantagenet Smith'*. Have a nice day!

Richard Green

NOTE TO EDITOR: PLEASE DO NOT CORRECT TYPOS OR

Infuriating Recipe No 17
DORSET PURPLE VINNEY

This is a cheese that that you will never forget making. It can only be produced in Dorset, so make sure you haven't strayed into Wiltshire or any other county before getting started.

Ingredients

1 small to large uncooked ham
A reasonable quantity of potatoes, new or old according to when they were harvested
1 red cabbage, fresh and firm
½lb – ½kg of raw beetroot (cooked will do if you are short of time, although this consideration is relative, as you will see)
2 lb large Moroccan prunes (difficult to find these days, but the village shop in Piddleminster Matravers stocks them – Mrs Harris, next door, has the opening times)
11 radishes
4 apricoticots
2 strips lemon (or orange) peal
3 gills red-wine vinegar
2 cloves Gaelic
1 lb soft-brown sagur
4.45 gal semi-skimmed cows' milk
a small pinch of penicillium roqueforti
lactic starter
vegetarian rennet (you can make your own from fig leaves, artichokes or melon – see Infuriating Recipes No 2, 'Vegetarian Rennet')
Salt, pepper and dandelion juice to taste

Method

Cook the ham according to Infuriating Recipe No 4 'Cooking a Ham'. The ingredients are included above to avoid confusion, just as they are for the prune-and-radish chutney, which you should now prepare, according to Infuriating Recipe No 19 'Prune and Radish Chutney' (due out in February).
Lightly scrottle the cabbage and simmer boldly in freshly drawn water until the   . Set the cabbage to one side (it doesn't matter which), but save the water. If you've already thrown it down the drain, I'm afraid you'll have to start again because it's the cabbage water we're after here. Using this, which should be a startling blue colour, boil the beetroot until tender (it will yield to a light sideways pressure applied with a steel or copper bodkin). Cooking will take anything from one to four hours, according to size. Again, set aside the beetroot and save the water, which should now enjoy a deep purple hue like indelible ink – I hope you're wearing an apron.

Before you did any of this, you should have started to make the cheese, using the time-worn secret recipe for Dorset Blue Vinney (obtainable, or unavailable from Woodbridge Farm near Sturminster Newton). Once the curdling stage is complete, blend in the 'ink' without prejudice and allow 56 hours for it to colour the mixture before proceeding to the draining, pressing and ripening stages, which will take a further 12 – 18 months (1 – 1 ½ years).
Meanwhile, invite a few non-vegetarian guests to a lunch, which will consist of the ham, served with boiled or mashed potato, red cabbage, beetroot and prune-and-radish chutney. You've probably realised all this is to use up the cooked cabbage and beetroot.
When the cheese is ready, you may wish to invite the same guests back (if they haven't moved away or died) to a re-union where everyone can sample your very own Dorset Purple Vinney, with Dorset nobs, such as Lord Phillips of Worth Matravers. I'm hoping one day to have time to try making the recipe myself.

Joan Barclay

ENID'S HOMELAND

A bloody battle holds the key
to Kingston Lacy's history;
Corfe Castle its proud monument
of power and fame and affluence.

(The Famous Five
did run amok
among its ruins
of solid rock.)

Cottage gardens host cream teas;
old pubs serve Dorset brew.
Quintessential Englishness,
with 'ooohs' and 'aaahs' on cue!

'tis Dorset with its bumpkins,
loved by the City gents.
All relax their glory
in blessed consequence.

Cove and cave, cliff and chine
evoking thoughts of God's design.
Rolling hills give way to sea,
a place to sense tranquillity.

Beryl Elizabeth Jupp

Inspired by a true incident some years ago on the cliffs of Dorset.

IN MEMORIAM

Three young people bonny and blithe,
jumped off the cliffs, fell and died.
Youngsters for whom life held no hope
immortalised in one swift stroke.

Between the three, two lads and a girl,
a dream of freedom began to unfurl.
It seemed to them that they might fly,
the reality was that they would die.

Perhaps they laughed as they made their way
to those awesome cliffs on that Summer's day;
when three young people, bonny and blithe,
jumped off the cliffs, fell and died ....

Susan Northcott

COTTAGE FOR SALE

'Here we are, No 1 Watery Lane.'

 The estate agent's voice sounded a little weary to Fay. Hardly surprising. This was the fourth cottage she and Miles had visited today after dismissing several others as not even worth viewing. Some looked quaint or picturesque from the outside but so far none had been what they wanted. This one was better – it even had a thatched roof.

 'The other cottages,' Mr Owens reminded them, 'weren't quite . . . ,' he paused for a few seconds to open the heavy wooden front door, 'what you wanted, but here you have many attractive features including an inglenook fireplace. Come on in.'

 Fay and Miles followed him into the living-room. The fireplace took up most of one wall with an enormous hearth under a blackened oak beam. Stone seats were built in either side of the open grate and a cat was curled up in one corner.

 Or was it? She blinked, no, just a shadow.

 'Ah yes,' Miles nodded. 'Lead on.'

 The room was low-ceilinged, predictably dark with small leaded windows, thick with atmosphere. Also damp, thought Fay, as she sniffed the stale air.

 'Hmmm,' said Miles, ducking to avoid the oak beams. 'So what's its history?'

 Mr Owens coughed. 'It's a typical Dorset cottage. Of course it does require modernisation, just as any 300-year-old cottage would, the previous owner lived here until very elderly. Thatched roof, small garden, outbuildings – a lot of potential. Then there's the field, about an eighth of an acre, good arable land, not a bad little package. You'll find some lovely walks alongside the river or up to the hills.'

 'What a weird tree,' Fay was staring through the window in amazement, 'it seems to be beckoning to us.' Overhanging the small barn, swaying in the wind, was a tangle of black branches overlaid with lichen. What sort of tree was it, she puzzled, hawthorn perhaps?

 Mr Owens didn't reply. He was already ushering them cautiously over the wooden floorboards towards the staircase. Each stair had a different groan or creak and above that Fay was sure she could hear some faint rustlings.

 'I hope there aren't mice,' she began, speaking extra loudly to allay her worries, 'we don't want to have to deal with them.'

35

'Mice? I doubt it,' Mr Owens replied, 'nothing for them here, is there? Anyway, you could easily sort them if you kept a cat.'

Upstairs, head lowered against the beams, Miles was exploring the bedrooms.

'Hmmm,' he repeated.

Fay could tell he was beginning to re-think his first impressions but as she crossed the room to the window she found herself looking down on the ancient tree again. It had changed. Now it seemed to be waving to her, trying to get her attention.

'Lovely,' she smiled at Mr Owens, 'this is just the sort of place we had in mind when we first discussed it, didn't we, Miles?'

'Hmmm,' said Miles, 'Not in my mind, not this exactly.' He turned and started down the stairs. 'Do we have time to look outside before it gets dark? I'd like to see round the barn and the other building, walk over the field, get my bearings. '

Fay smiled. Miles hated being driven about, now he wanted a walk. Mr Owens pulled back the sleeve of his waxed jacket, glanced at his watch and pulled in his lips. 'Hmmm.'

It seems to be catching, thought Fay.

'Hmmm,' he said again, 'I rather wanted to catch up with a client who lives in the next village. How long d'you think you'll be? Half an hour, forty minutes?' He paused and glanced at his watch again. 'I could be there and back while you're taking it in. You're sure you really don't mind if I shoot off then?'

'No, that's fine.'

Fay was studying the cast-iron fireplace. Lying in bed at night with the firelight casting a rosy glow would be very romantic. On the other hand, there was no proper bathroom, just a washbasin and dripping tap. Getting the plumbing sorted would be a major project in itself.

She turned to speak to Miles and found herself alone in the room. She looked at the wooden corner cupboard. Could be full of moths. She walked over, pulled it open and found – nothing. Only an old book. She picked it up. A Bible, with an inscription on the flyleaf. Not easy to read without a magnifying glass and a good light, still, she'd examine it later.

'I'm going outside,' Miles' voice came floating upstairs. 'This kitchen needs a fair bit of work, but that's your department, darling.'

'Thanks.'

Back downstairs Fay could see what he meant. As a kitchen it was utterly basic, only the stone sink was worth keeping. The scrubbed pine table under the window looked quite rickety while in the corner a wooden rocking chair moved slightly. Comfy though, she thought, if the black cat asleep on its sagging cushions was anything to go by.

'Another cat ...'

'Where?' Miles' head appeared through the open window.

'Oh – no, not a real one, I was just thinking ...'

'You could have a cat, but a dog would be better – walks by the river and all that.'

Miles was already striding ahead to the field. Fay rubbed her eyes. She was getting tired; it had been a long day. Outside she picked her way over the paved yard and past the small barn. The twisted tree grew right by the entrance, like a sentry on guard. She opened the door cautiously. Inside was so dark she could make nothing out. She hesitated on the threshold.

'Come on in, dearie, don't be fright.' An odd little chuckle. Then Fay was banging the door shut, running back to the normality of the house. Inside she sank into the rocking chair waiting for her breathing to calm down. She didn't believe in spirits but this house was definitely playing tricks on her.

A noise caught her attention and she went back outdoors giving the barn a wide berth. She could see Miles shouting and waving to her

across the field, trying to tell her he'd seen something. She hurried on. He was running now, glancing back over his shoulder, shouting more loudly, shooing her back with his hands. 'No! Don't come any closer, it looks dangerous, that bull. I thought it was fenced in but ...'

Red-faced and puffing badly he reached the gate before she did and started to climb over it.

'Careful,' Fay shouted, 'look out for that loose wire.'

'What?' Miles turned his head as he climbed, caught his foot in the tangled wire and fell awkwardly against the metal bars.

'Aaarrh!' His scream of pain echoed through the hills.

'Miles, darling, don't move!' Fay's brain was scrambling through her rusty collection of first-aid training. 'I'll ring 999 to get you a doctor, an ambulance, but you have to stay still; moving will only make things worse.'

'Don't move?' Miles was lying face down in the mud, 'I'm not staying here. Help me roll over and sit up.'

Together they managed to get him to a more comfortable position leaning back on the gate.

'I'll run back to the house,' said Fay, 'my mobile's in my bag – where's yours?'

Miles felt in his pocket. 'Not here. Just do something quickly, I'm in agony – think I'm going to be sick.'

Fay studied his white face. He looked as if he might go into shock. She took off her jacket and covered his legs. There wasn't much else she could do here, she had to go back to the house.

Inside she dialled 999 on her mobile. No signal. She went outside and tried again. Still no signal and no sign of Mr Owens. Indoors again she tore a page from the house details and scribbled a note on the back then tucked it under the cast iron knocker on the front door.

If only there were electricity, but of course that had been turned off like the water. Then she remembered the dripping tap upstairs. Maybe not. She tried the tap on the kitchen sink and after a few coughs water flowed. She opened a cupboard at random. Inside were dusty but reasonably clean glasses, they would do with a rinse. But what to give him?

Miles needed a painkiller badly and she'd taken her last two paracetamol after drinking too much country cider at the pub last night. She tried the other cupboards – empty. The only other possibility was the little barn. She had to brave that dark, spooky atmosphere. Miles was depending on her.

Steeling herself against spirits, spiders or mice, she cautiously opened the barn door. To her relief, this time it seemed ordinary, not frightening, more welcoming. She propped the door open to allow more light in and saw just inside a storm lantern with a candle and a box of matches. With the lamp lit, Fay could see an array of shelves running the length of the building and at the far end a heap of branches and logs. Walking further in she explored the shelves with a growing sense of curiosity. Hundreds of jars were lined up in some sort of order, possibly alphabetical, the labels so worn and dusty it was difficult to tell.

She picked up one or two jars and tried to decipher the handwriting. *Valerian, Dandelion, Salix, Camomile, Comfrey.* These seemed a little newer, perhaps the former occupant had used them for cooking. She took them back into the kitchen and stood them on the table next to the old Bible. Now what?

'Please, help me, and Miles. I don't know what to do.' Who were her words trying to reach? Someone, anyone. She stood still, hands on the table, concentrating. The fog of muddled thought in her head slowly lifted and a voice came through. *Move Miles, try to make a crutch.*

She hurried back to the log pile – no time to worry about spiders now – selecting a sturdy length of birch with a slight fork at one end.

'Miles, sit up! You can't stay here on the ground any longer. Hold onto the gate and I'll help you stand on your good leg. Then it's just a few steps to the house.'

Fay could see his teeth chattering. The spring sunshine had gone, replaced by a cold-edged breeze.

'It's no good, it hurts too much, let me stay here till the ambulance arrives, they'll know what to do.'

'No, you need warmth. It's not far.'

Using all her strength, Fay dragged him upright, thrusting the branch under his armpit, thankful he was wearing a thick jacket. Talking loudly to encourage him, she got him into the house. She moved the rocking chair close to the fireplace and sat him down, then ran back out and grabbed an armful of logs. She built up a criss-cross of smaller pieces before adding the larger logs, pleased to find the wood dry enough to burn well.

She tried her mobile again. Still no signal and still no Mr Owens. Fay looked at the jars. Dare she risk some ancient herbal medicine or would it make things worse?

Look in the book. That voice again.

She hesitated, was she going mad with worry? The only book in the house was the Bible. She opened its pages at random, the thin leaves flickered through her fingers like silk but there were one or two that seemed thicker, stronger. She looked closer. Stuck to the reverse of these were smaller pieces of paper covered in tiny handwriting – an A to Z of herbs and their uses.

Comfrey, Fay read. *Make a poultice with its leaves and place on swelling.* She'd need hot water for that. If only there were a kettle or saucepans.

Look in the barn. Out again and there she saw just what she needed, tucked in behind the branches. A heavy metal cauldron complete with chains and a large hook. Fay carried it back to the house, rinsed off the dust and put in some clean water. Carefully she hung it over the fire.

Miles had more colour now he'd warmed up but was still cursing under his breath with the pain. Fay went back to the handwritten notes. *Salix*, wasn't that it? Yes, willow and willow bark was what they used for pain and inflammation before it was packaged as *Aspirin*. She took the top off the jar. *Add to water and swallow.* It was already ground up, so she shook a little into a glass.

She took the mixture back to Miles with some clean water to wash it down. Thinking ahead to the poultice, she remembered stories of heroines tearing up their petticoats for bandages. Not possible with jeans. All she had were clean tissues but there was a curtain on the upstairs window. It would have to do – boiling water would kill any germs.

So busy was she that darkness had crept up on the cottage before she noticed. At last Miles was relatively comfortable in the chair and getting sleepy from the warmth. Soon she'd have to get some more logs for the fire. But first she needed to study the inscription in the Bible. She had nearly finished when a knock at the door roused her.

'Hello,' Mr Owens pushed it open and came inside, his face a mixture of worry and surprise. 'I'm sorry I took so long but my car broke down – it took forever to walk back and borrow another–'

He stopped as he saw Miles sprawled in the chair next to the fire.

'What on earth have you two been up to?'

Fay gave him a piercing stare. 'Why didn't you tell us this used to be Cauldron Cottage, old Hetty's home? Lucky for us she was a white witch and a very helpful one, too. Now will you take us to the nearest hospital, please, before I'm tempted to turn you into a toad?'

Anne Peterson

POOLE AND HER LIGHTHOUSE

Here in Poole, this ancient port,
long a holiday resort,
shoppers swarm the level crossing,
sailboats on the Harbour tossing,
water sports to watch or try,
as back and forth the ferries ply.
Visitors explore the Quay,
view the famous Pottery.

Poole is Bournemouth's older sister,
just as bright without the glister –
with her gleaming, on-shore Lighthouse,
cultural beacon, quite the right house
for the BSO and all the arts –
coachloads come from many parts.
See the building, oh so cool,
when at dusk it lights up Poole.

John Barclay

IN DORSET. . .

D readful, dark and devilish deeds were done

O rdnance opposed officialdom, with onerous

outcome

R evenue on Rum Royalty rightly requested

S mugglers silently stowed stashes sequestered

E king out existence, escaping excise

T ea taxed, treason and treachery thrived . . .

. . . in Dorset.

Mike Lawrence

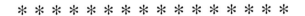

While dining in Sturminster Newton,
a pensioner choked on a crouton.
  With soup he was spattered.
  It wouldn't have mattered,
but he had his best Sunday suit on.

A commuter residing in Wool,
was cruelly chased by a bull
  all the way to the station,
  but, to his vexation,
the train on the platform was full.

John Barclay

THE PURBECK PLOUGHING MATCH

It had been advertised as 'between Wool and Lulworth', so I naïvely assumed it was a contest between a team from Wool and a team from Lulworth. It turned out that it was between individuals on a <u>site</u> between Wool and Lulworth.

At half past nine, the October day was bright and clear with warm sunshine and a sharp wind that made my cheeks glow. I parked my car beside one of the many lorries that had brought tractors for the competition. Lulworth Castle Estate had made available three fields of sweetcorn stubble, a total of more than 60 acres.

It was a charming scene with clumps of trees around the edge of the site and red, blue and green tractors dotted about like 'Dinky' toys. The motors purred continuously. A little boy, who loved tractors, was of course in Heaven. Unlike most big open-air events, there was no PA system to mar the peace. I was one of the few 'incomers' among a gathering largely made up of local families and I heard rural accents as broad as a sow's arse. Twenty-two trophies, with intriguing titles like the 'Hunting Lubricants Cup', the 'Sugar Beet Tankard' and the 'Discussion Cup' were set out on a table to gleam in the sun and spur the contestants to greater efforts.

This was the 28th annual ploughing match in Purbeck. It was organised by the Wareham & Purbeck Young Farmers Club and the Purbeck Vintage Ploughing Committee. There were 64 individual entrants in ten classes – from the horticultural cultivator that you walk behind like a lawnmower, to the mighty six-furrow reversible plough. I read the rules twice but still couldn't understand them. I spoke to some of the experienced spectators but the more they explained the technicalities the more confused I got. The judges had their work cut out to get round all the plots and inspect the work at key stages of the ploughing. But they did pause to explain to me what they were looking for, 'A straight line; all the soil to be turned over – the surface debris to be buried; and the soil not to be dug too deep – or you end with a heap'.

For townies like me, I should explain that ploughing is simply the process of cutting the surface and turning the top layer of soil over, a process which moves it to one side, leaving a trough on one side of the strip and a ridge on the other. When you plough the next strip, this trough gets filled in but a new one is created. As the process continues there is always one trough and one ridge – until the last strip is ploughed when, if you've planned the operation properly, you

turn the remaining ridge into the final ditch leaving the whole surface even – easier said than done!

A reversible plough has two banks of blades, pivoting around a main beam and operated hydraulically. One bank turns the soil to the left the other to the right. This means that the person ploughing can make a U-turn at the edge of the plot, switch the opposite bank of blades into play and join up immediately with the work just completed. These big commercial machines can plough an acre in about ten minutes and it's a delight to watch a 'six-furrow reversible' making the soil turn over in curves as graceful as a leaping salmon. To make the competition tougher for this class, each contestant was required to plough part of his plot on the diagonal.

For those working with small, traditional machinery on the other hand it is a labour of love. These competitors were hard put to plough a straight furrow on ground baked during a hot dry summer and studded with tough corn stumps.

Contestants kept stopping and leaping from their tractors to adjust the settings of their ploughs. Some of the trailing ploughs had to be weighted to make them cut deep enough. In the novice class, there was a boy of thirteen, followed on foot by someone I took to be his grandfather who, from time to time, would ride on the plough to hold it down.

44

A veteran contestant had been competing for fifty years. Another old hand had built his own tractor from spare parts, especially for competitions. A young woman competing in the 'Vintage Mounted' class, her blond hair blown all over the place, had a fluffy toy fixed to one of the mudguards of her tractor by way of a mascot. I saw her stop to check the depth of the furrow. Later I watched her stand at the edge of the plot, look back over her line, then stride around with measuring rods and place stakes in the ground to guide her.

From a mobile café I bought fish and chips and a cup of tea, which I enjoyed in the sun sitting on the end of a trailer. I talked to a pack of cub reporters from Reuters News Agency, who were spending a training week in the area finding, researching and writing up stories, and taking photographs.

Everyone was invited to guess the weight (67lb 2oz) of an ugly brute of a pumpkin, so big I could hardly lift it. The prize was a basket of fruit. The pumpkin itself was auctioned off for five pounds. A local firm had donated 500 litres of tractor fuel, which went for 75 pounds.

The draw for the raffle took ages because there were so many prizes. The main prize-giving took a long time too because in some of the classes even the person who came fifth was called up. The prizes were presented by Sarah Weld, representing the Lulworth Estate. The Committee Secretary, Helen Selby had the harder job of handing her the right prizes, after a morning spent competing in the 'Vintage Mounted' class and no doubt weeks of preparations before the event. She told me she hoped the day would raise £1,000 for the Dorset and Somerset Air Ambulance.

Next year, entrants will compete just for the honour instead of for numerous small money prizes, so the Match should raise even more for charity. I cannot think that the change will put contestants off, for I'm sure they enter for the love of their skill and the fun and fellowship of the day. This year's overall champion, Trevor Miles, is now entitled to go forward to next year's 'British National' match.

While instant gratification, electronic communications, virtual reality and 'reality shows' are threatening to take over our lives, the ploughing match is a valuable reminder of a traditional culture based on skilled outdoor physical work. It would be difficult to find a happier, more wholesome outing for the family or one more deeply rooted in our rural heritage.

John Barclay

This article first appeared in the Purbeck Gazette in November 2003. Today, the Ploughing Match is still going strong.

CRUSTY OLD BUCCANEER SEEKS
RETIRED LADY PIRATE

Yo ho ho! I'm a merry Dorset pirate,
one of the nicest men you could meet –
if you don't mind the 'orrible breath
and the smell of me dirty old feet.

I don't 'ave a parrot on me shoulder
'cos I've never sailed tropical seas.
Besides I'm allergic to feathers
and a bird that close makes me sneeze.

I've always hated the old skull and cross bones –
never been my idea of a flag;
and I don't keep me treasure in a chest
as I prefer a trendy sports bag.

Like all pirates, I've done a few naughty things.
There's no way you would call me a saint.
I told me crew I was really quite good,
but they insisted 'Oh, no you ain't.'

Now I'm retired, homeless, without a ship.
So I wander up and down the street,
frightening kids and telling stories,
with a bottle of Badgers for a treat.

Mike Lawrence

A SPECIAL FRIEND

'Brace yourself,' said Vicki. 'Remember he's one of my oldest friends and I've been his secret admirer since I was six.'

Colin grinned. 'Lord, I'm feeling a bit nervous. D'you think I'll measure up?'

'Don't ask me, please.' Vicki laughed. 'You tell me after you've met him. Come on, we'd better hurry, we've got to get to Gran's after this.'

Grabbing his hand she set the pace up the firm chalk path, worn over centuries by visiting couples and tourists. After a few minutes she paused, took a deep breath, then said, 'Please, Colin, not a word to Gran. I know she'll like you but she doesn't approve of all my friends.'

Jane set the table for three, using her best china and cutlery. Soon her granddaughter would arrive for lunch, accompanied by her boyfriend, a fellow university lecturer. He was not the first boyfriend to be introduced to her but Jane had a feeling, picked up from her chats with Vicki, that this was 'the one'. She was relieved that for their first meeting Colin was just coming for the day as she was a bit unsure what to provide if he were staying overnight. In her young days it happened, of course, but secretly, not in the parents' or grandparents' houses and at least the couple would have been engaged. Nowadays, many young people didn't even bother with formalities – engagements then marriage. No, she must stop pondering and get on with perfecting the pudding, and not just that – she should force herself into the twenty-first century.

While whipping the cream, her attention was caught by the sunlight's effect on the small willow tree in her back garden. Glinting on the wet, grey catkins it transformed them into pearls. Close by, gold strings were gently falling from a hazel tree; they'd done their work and would be appreciated by birds in the autumn. An omen, she thought, *of better things to come* and soon they would. An hour later, she took the casserole out of the Aga as she was afraid it might get too dry. She glanced at her watch – nearly one o'clock but Vicki had said they'd arrive about midday. It was unlike her to be late. Perhaps there was a hold-up on the A30. Charlie, the Cocker spaniel, gave a short bark and hurried from the room. A second later Jane heard voices in the hall and into the kitchen came Vicki accompanied by her boyfriend.

'Sorry we're a bit late, Gran,' she said, hugging her. 'This is Colin.'

While shaking hands and exchanging traditional formalities, Jane observed that Colin was taller than Vicki – rightly so – and had good features and a shock of rich, brown hair. Both he and Vicki looked well with flushed cheeks and bright eyes. Vicki's soft fair hair looked windswept.

'Were you held up?' Jane asked, putting dishes on the table. 'Oh thank you, Colin.'

He had put two bottles of wine on the dresser, one white and one red.

'We had a short walk, Gran. Hope you don't mind but more rain is expected later and Colin is intrigued by the village.'

'Well, he is another historian,' responded Jane, beaming, 'and this is one of the most interesting villages in Dorset.'

'It certainly is,' Colin enthused. 'The remains of the beautiful Abbey, lovely old cottages, like this one and, well, a truly unique...'

'Lunch is ready,' interrupted Vicki. 'Please will you uncork the wine, Colin?'

During the meal, which was greatly appreciated, the talk was about history and archaeology and the luck the two young people had in finding jobs at the university. Nearly two hours passed, then they settled with their coffee in front of the log fire, alight despite spring having arrived. The forecast rain was now falling relentlessly and the temperature had dropped. When not sprawled on the hearthrug Charlie rested his muzzle on Colin's knee, clearly accepting him.

'Lucky Vicki spending most of her childhood here,' said Colin.

'And lucky me,' said Jane. 'I love my son dearly but having Vicki with me was like acquiring a daughter in my middle years. At Sherborne she refused to be a boarder and, as her parents worked overseas, it was the best solution.'

'And now she's only down the road. Exeter's not too far away,' said Colin.

'Wait 'til Summer comes – it won't seem so close then,' said Jane. 'Piles of tourists' cars on the road.'

Colin grinned. 'Why are they going to Devon and Cornwall when there's a lovely place like this?'

'Oh, we get our share.'

Colin accepted a second cup of coffee then, with Jane's approval, put another log on the fire.

'This is wonderful,' he said, 'I love such comfort.'

'But you're an outdoor man,' said Jane, laughing.

48

'I am, and not all outdoor men get this luck. Not here.' He was grinning and looking at Vicki who seemed to be concealing a smile as she turned away.

Only two days later Jane picked up the phone, wagging a finger at barking Charlie.

'Gran, thanks for that lovely visit. I've some news – Colin and I are engaged.'

'Oh, darling, that's wonderful. Do your dad and mum know?'

'Yes, and delighted. They're coming over in two weeks for the engagement party and Colin's parents and brother are coming from Shropshire. I'll ring you once we've got all the arrangements sorted. It'll be down here.'

In September, the wedding took place in Jane's local church. She was thrilled and her son and daughter-in-law had no objection – after all their child had spent longer in her gran's village than theirs. The service was beautiful. How Jane's late husband would have loved it. Sadly, he never knew his granddaughter, having said *farewell* to life in the Falklands War. Yet Vicki made sure he was referred to in the mention of *absent friends*, bringing strong feelings of pride and love to many in the congregation.

A year passed – a good year for Jane – with lots of family visits, a trip to her son and daughter-in-law in Dubai and several to Exeter. Then came a call from Vicki at midday and, unusually, on a working day.

'Are you all right, darling? You sound a bit stressed.'

'Gran, I'd only tell this to you. You know Colin is older than I am – well, we decided not to wait to start a family and nothing's happened.'

'But you've been married quite a short time and you are both still young.'

'I know but there is a permanent problem, Gran, all due to mumps in adolescence and…'

'Yes, I know what it can do but there's so much help available nowadays. Have you consulted anyone?'

'Yes, that's how we found out about the problem.'

'Well good luck with the next stage, darling.'

'Thanks, but I hope we don't have to go that far. Oh, and thanks for your message, Gran. We'll see you on Saturday.'

Arriving in time for lunch, which was Colin's treat for the 'girls' at the ancient pub, they then walked with Charlie alongside the small river until teatime was called. Jane was relieved that both Colin and Vicki seemed relaxed.

Later, Vicki commented, 'You look tired Gran. Are you okay?'

'Almost. That horrid bout of flu took its toll. Not sleeping was the worst part but Doctor James has given me some really effective sleeping pills. I need to get some sleep particularly when I've a class in the morning.'

'Of course, you're still teaching music,' said Colin. 'That's great. I loved the piece you played for Vicki's birthday.'

Jane laughed. 'Debussy's *The Girl with the Flaxen Hair*. Appropriate, I suppose. Now, I'll love you and leave you and hope you sleep well.'

The important phone call came nine weeks later. Jane was teaching a Grade Three pupil so she picked the phone up at the end of the lesson. The message was: *Gran, please ring me as soon as possible. Love you. Vicki.* Of course she rang immediately, feeling a shade apprehensive.

'Oh great to hear you, Gran. I've wonderful news – I'm pregnant.'

'Oh darling, I'm thrilled. Give my love and congratulations to Colin. So you got some invaluable help.'

There was a moment's silence then a giggle. 'Gran, we did get help only not the sort you'd approve of. Remember, when I was six you said "Never go near him, or even glance at him"?'

'You don't mean that disgusting… But you can't get close anymore.'

'You can if you've the nerve. Please don't be cross.'

'Cross! I'm delighted for you both.'

'Good. We'll see you very soon. Must go as I've a seminar coming up. 'Bye Gran and lots of love.'

Not used to shaky legs Jane sat down by the hall table and took a few deep breaths. She closed her eyes and immediately a vision came of that visit when she'd had an early night, had taken sleeping pills then, unusually, had been awoken by Charlie about five a.m.

'So sorry, Gran, just been to the loo and must have disturbed him,' Vicki had quietly called from the landing.

Several hours later, as they were leaving, she'd noticed Colin pulling a bulging rucksack onto his shoulder, not his usual overnight bag. She forced herself into the present, got up and went to the kitchen where she made a strong cup of tea. Charlie sat beside her, staring rather than looking, his eyes bright with anticipation.

'All right, our walk is a bit overdue,' she said. 'Best fetch your lead.'

Twenty minutes later Charlie was behaving as if he were two not twelve. Eagerly he looked around the unfamiliar area, alert to every sound. He greeted an approaching collie with a friendly bark

The couple with the dog smiled and the woman said, 'Lovely area. Wonderful view.'

The man was grinning broadly. 'My wife's really impressed.' Both were now laughing as they walked on, downhill. Relieved to be alone, Jane leaned on the fence, looking across the wide valley. The chap was unchanged apart from being a bit tidier. The club was still held threateningly in his right hand and the other was empty and flung wide. As for the rest – all was revealed, as blatant as ever.

Jane stared reluctantly for a minute then she relaxed. With Charlie's eyes fixed on her, she said aloud, 'I'm grateful to you, Cerne Giant. You've lived up to your reputation.' Then she blew him a kiss. Charlie gave a short bark but whether of approval or otherwise she couldn't tell and didn't care.

Pauline Morphy

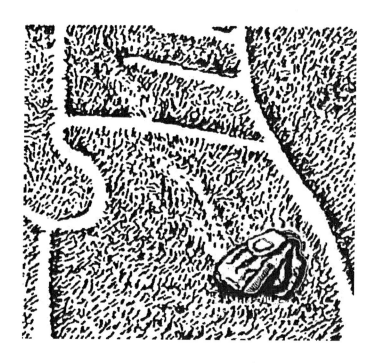

THE SWANAGE RAILWAY

In the optimistic days of Queen Victoria,
at a time of rail expansion – nay, euphoria –
by an act of parliament, the brave John Mowlem,
who to win support of MPs would cajole 'em,
set 'in train' a scheme to connect Swanage nicely
to the main line by a branch opened precisely
six score years ago, when bargain-price excursions
brought in crowds to the resort and its diversions.

For eighty years both passenger and freight trains plied
the route to Swanage through the peaceful countryside;
but then road transport stole the business from the train,
while families flew off on package tours to Spain.
Around the country, branch lines fell into decline
and British Railways closed (alas!) the Swanage Line.
They pulled up all the track; and railway lovers sighed,
to see that what was once a busy branch had died.

The line had not lain long within its rusty grave
before some true enthusiasts began to save
the Swanage Railway bit by bit, till quite restored an'
back in operation all the way to Norden.
What a labour this of love – o'er thirty years!
Today a team of full-time staff and volunteers,
'mid acrid smoke and belching steam, turn back the page
of history, transport us to a grander age.

The cheery, helpful service that the staff provide
recalls the age of steam as much as does the ride.
The railway line that brought in tourists at its height
still does – for it's a tourist draw in its own right.
The last remaining sections of the track – to Wareham
on the main line – have been tackled to prepare 'em
for the one outstanding challenge that remains –
to link the Swanage Railway up with South West Trains!

John Barclay

CHANGING LIVES

Laughter is infectious; happiness is envied; joy is visible. How often do these attributes turn heads – perhaps to make the onlooker think and wonder? Or perhaps to envy what has caused so much wellbeing. It is often said that when a person commits himself to the wellbeing of his fellow human, then the world is a better place.

This is the story of a venture in Poole, started over eighteen years ago, brought about by a chance meeting of the owner of an island in Poole Harbour and someone involved with water skiing for disabled people.

These like-minded individuals, she with an island and he with know-how, both had the idea of organising and offering holidays for disabled and disadvantaged people. And so the **Green Island Holiday Trust** was born. As a result, about 35 holidaymakers a year, with all sorts of disabilities, many wheelchair users, were loaded onto a boat, taken to the Island and cared for by people from all walks of life, willing to give a week of their time to look after others. And the idea worked – wonderfully, magically.

A few years ago, Green Island was sold and a new home eventually found at Holton Lee near Wareham – 365 acres of glorious woodland, open spaces, views of Poole Harbour and breath-taking sunsets. The holidays still follow the same format, with activities such as boat trips (on our own specially adapted boat), art and pottery days, bird watching, carriage driving, trips on the Swanage railway and fun entertainment in the evening.

Offer five holidaymakers, with six carers, these experiences and, whatever the weather, the sounds of laughter and happiness will always be heard. Amazing things happen, such as the wheelchair user being able to water-ski, the blind person to steer a boat or the artist to paint without using his hands for the first time. Imagine the sheer joy of that tearful moment when a young man, whose only method of communicating was by **winking**, with one wink said 'hello!' to another wink.

We need, for a while, to live as we wish,
with a freedom from pain and care,
with a giddiness of heart
of mind and of soul,
as free as a bird in the air.
To taste the flavours of new experiences,
to spread wings and believe we can fly.
A chance to throw off inhibitions,
to be free, ourselves, and untied.

Where else do we have time to eat then?
Where else do we have time to share?
Where else do we have time to doze then?
Where else do we have time to care?
Green Island allows free spirits to roam,
a chance to be you or me,
to sail with the wind, to fly with the birds
in our own world of dreams, to be **free**!

Margaret Terrey

ODE TO DURDLE DOOR

Such beauteous coastline defending our land,
where crags hold deep secrets of former times,
the sea licks at your footholds causing erosion;
then smashes in waves of rhythmical rhymes.

Your obdurate rock allows structure of doorways;
exposed stones and shells, sculptured with skill
by nature's deft role, as they ebb to and fro.
When a storm has subsided, all becomes still.

Nothing has moved you away from this place,
our fortress, protector . . . your call is alluring.
My heart longs and yearns to gaze on the ocean;
I arrive on your cliff top and sense an outpouring.

Historical ramparts revealing the layers
of ages long gone. They call you Jurassic.
Will we ever know all the secrets you hide?
You remain closed and ordered; nigh on monastic.

I let go and drink in your grandiose beauty,
and marvel within as I walk at your side;
in awe of your sounds, your pure smell and your might;
powerless before you, my feet tread your tide.

Beryl Elizabeth Jupp

The Bakers

JOHN BARCLAY is a writer, performance poet and public speaker. He was educated at Bryanston School in Blandford. A former company speechwriter for Marks & Spencer, he moved to Wareham in 1998. For six years he wrote a light-hearted column for the Purbeck Gazette. In 2005, he brought out a book of poems, 'The Blood of Others'. He has won poetry slams in Bournemouth and Poole.

In his 'Poetry à la Carte', he performs pieces chosen by members of the audience from a menu of his work and popular poems by others. He is currently preparing a book of children's poems. John has written plays, song lyrics and comedy material.

In 2012, he published 'Surface Male', a book about his travels round the world without flying. For more information, please visit: www. johnbarclayink.com.

ALISON GREEN teaches academic writing skills at Bournemouth University and currently supports students with learning differences such as dyslexia and dyspraxia. She has facilitated creative writing workshops in Dorset and also in the south of France where she spent a sabbatical year. Excerpts from her letters written during *l'année sabbatique* have been read on local radio and to other audiences. She is published in a range of media including academic journals, *Dorset Life*, local press, national websites and edited and contributed to the journal, *Peninsular*. Alison is guest writer at http://creative-frontiers.com/ and her own blog is at http://donaldandtheweasels.wordpress.com/ Contact Alison at: aligreen52@hotmail.com

RICHARD GREEN has been writing since he was a boy and is still scribbling away at an age, 63, when he should know better. Much of his output has been poetry but recently he has been concentrating on short stories. Some folk regard his work as 'outlandish', 'bizarre' or just plain 'weird'. But Richard says he merely tells it as he sees it.

Richard has lived in Dorset for over 40 years so he is still a newcomer. The county is near enough to the Big City to be accessible by Iron Horse (or in wet weather dug-out canoe) and though eastern areas are becoming increasingly suburbanised there is still plenty of unspoilt beauty in remoter parts to make it still recognisable as the county of Barnes and Hardy – but to be on the safe side, Richard never ventures west of Dorchester or north of Blandford without an armed guard. Contact e-mail: green61@gmail.com.

BERYL ELIZABETH JUPP came to live in Dorset in 1961. She married Dave in 1964. They brought up their three daughters in Poole. There are now three granddaughters and four grandsons. Family life and a personal faith, she says, have formed a firm basis for her journey through life.

Writing has always given Beryl pleasure and poetry is her first love. It is to her: an outlet in grief; moving when exploring human depths that provoke thought, and good for the soul when funny. She enjoys 'running off' a ditty for friends when the occasion arises. She is also keenly interested in scriptwriting, in particular period drama and situation comedy.

In retirement, Wimborne is home to Beryl (and Dave). They enjoy walking and gardening. Being involved in family life brings great joy.

MIKE LAWRENCE was born, bred and worked in North London, moving to Dorset in the sixties. Now retired, he composes and performs poems and writes short stories. He was the 2012 winner at the Morley Literature Festival.

'As a small boy,' he says, 'I found telling jokes defused threats from bullies.' At school he was hopeless at maths, so when he left, he worked for an insurance company, two finance houses and as a vehicle accident estimator, 'just to get his own back'. In his spare time, Mike performed as one half of a children's clown act, a magician and an impressionist.

Mike enters literary competitions all over the UK because without their deadlines, 'None of my work would be finished and it forces me to write about a vast range of subjects and themes that I'd never think of myself.'

LIZ MAGEE When she was at school the English teacher did not manage to ignite for her an interest in poetry and it was not until she attended a creative writing class in Dublin many years later that she started to enjoy it. She likes reading and writing poetry that obeys the rules and poetry that doesn't. She belongs to the Poole Poetry Group and Speakeasy, which gives her the opportunity to share what she has written, and enjoys the challenge of perfomance poetry. She won the Purbeck Art Weeks Poetry Slam in 2013.

She retired a few years ago from working with adults and children with learning difficulties and now theoretically has more time for all sorts of other creative activities, particularly painting. She lives in Poole and finds writing and painting a way to "hold the moment" in this beautiful part of the world.

SUSAN NORTHCOTT has always been a writer, journalist and poet. Her poetry, including the poems included in this anthology are motivated by unforgettable incidents and the events and emotions that lead up to them.

She enjoys poetry slams, open mics, festivals, etc. and interaction with audiences at these events. She has participated in events as diverse as 'roving poet' at Dorchester Fringe Festival and performing at the Nuyorican Poets Cafe, New York, as part of American Poetry Month, 2009.

Susan has lived in Dorset for 30 years providing ample scope for her other passions of open-water swimming, winter sea swimming with the Bournemouth Spartans, walking in our beautiful countryside and watching film as a member of the Lighthouse, Poole film club. She is also proud to be a patron of the Purbeck Film Festival and gains immense pleasure from participating in the annual Bournemouth Arts by the Sea Festival.

PAULINE MORPHY has an MA in Creative and Critical Writing and has had articles and short stories published. Her children's pony novel, *Exiles from the Moor*, first published in 1998 and recently republished, is raising money for the charity, World Horse Welfare. An enthusiast of the story is the world famous author and animal lover, Jilly Cooper, whose words are on the cover.

Under the Icing, an adults' novel, largely informed by Pauline's professional background in social work and counselling, is available as a Kindle ebook and paperback from Amazon.

She has run writing workshops at Mere School as part of the Mere Literary Festival and is a keen member of Pennybank Writers.

Born in Dorset she is a huge fan of Thomas Hardy and William Barnes and her main hobbies, beside writing and reading, are riding and painting.

ANNE PETERSON is a poet and writer who enjoys humour, particularly in performance poetry, as well as more serious work. She has won and been placed in many competitions and her poems and short stories have been published on the internet and in magazines.

Her writing career began in public relations writing newsletters and press releases. After moving to Dorset she worked in Poole Museums before gaining an MA in Creative and Critical Writing and completing a novel. Anne has published a collection of humorous verse and a children's book. She is also part of SOUTH poetry magazine's team, handling typesetting and design.

Anne is a member of Poole Writers' Circle, where she gives occasional poetry workshops, and also runs Speakeasy. She enjoys painting, gardening and is now working on her second novel set in Bulgaria.

MARGARET TERREY was born and raised in Bournemouth in the thirties. She was educated in a church school and a grammar school, where five years of Latin gave her an interest in semantics. She did nursing training at Westminster Hospital and worked as a nurse in New England until the sixties, when she returned to the UK.. She retired from nursing in 1999.

Margaret now lives in Boscombe. She loves poetry and likes to enter poetry competitions. She is a regular contributor to a church magazine.

M C WOOD (Mary Catherine Wood) has always been a bookworm and has always written. She had writing in various magazines from the age of ten, but her first short story was published by Collins in 1955; she was seventeen. After school, she read joint honours in English Literature and Graphic Art, with Mathematics as a subsidiary.

On retirement from teaching, Mary began to paint again, but as increasing arthritis made this difficult, she gradually turned to writing, this time mostly poetry – 'it's shorter!' Having had work printed in magazines, she self-published a book of poetry, 'Day Return'.

She has lived in Dorset for many years, gardening and writing, and, since her husband died, leads a quiet life with her dogs, who take her by the Stour, where she enjoys watching the otters, kingfishers, herons, egrets and other wildlife. Her main attribute is curiosity.

✳ ✳ ✳ ✳ ✳ ✳ ✳ ✳ ✳ ✳ ✳ ✳ ✳ ✳ ✳ ✳

Acknowledgements

We are particularly indebted to Tim Naish, who provided the marvellous line drawings and the cover for this anthology.

TIM NAISH used to visit his grandparents in Bridport as a child in the early sixties. He moved from Surrey to Dorset in the late nineties. He draws every day and is never without a sketchbook.
Contact Tim – timnsh9@gmail.com.

The drawings on pages 34 and 55 are by Anne Peterson and Edna Carter respectively.

Speakeasy Wimborne would like to thank all its sponsors and contributors.